THIS GIRL
Can Do Anything

Stephanie Stansbie • Hazel Quintanilla

LiTTLE TiGER

LONDON

I am

Ruby.

And I

know

what I

want.

Sometimes other people don't agree.

I think you need a coat, Ruby!

But I'm just being

I am **Ruby** and I know who I am.
These are the things **I am not**:

~~Buttercup~~

~~Angel~~

Sweet-Cheeks

Cutie-Pie

Once in a while, I am

Button

but **only**
when I feel like it.

I am **Ruby.**

And I
can do
anything.

Nothing's
going to
Stop
me.

NO GIRLS ALLOWED

Look! I am an

artist

but people don't always
understand me.

I am **ahead** of my time.

I am Ruby
and I
know
what I
want.

Today I want
to *fly*

but it's **not**
working.

So I have a little
lie down.

Mum says,

Do you want to try again?

Which is a bit **silly** because **of course I do!**

Nothing's going to stop me.

WHEEEE!

I am Ruby

and I

know

what I

like.

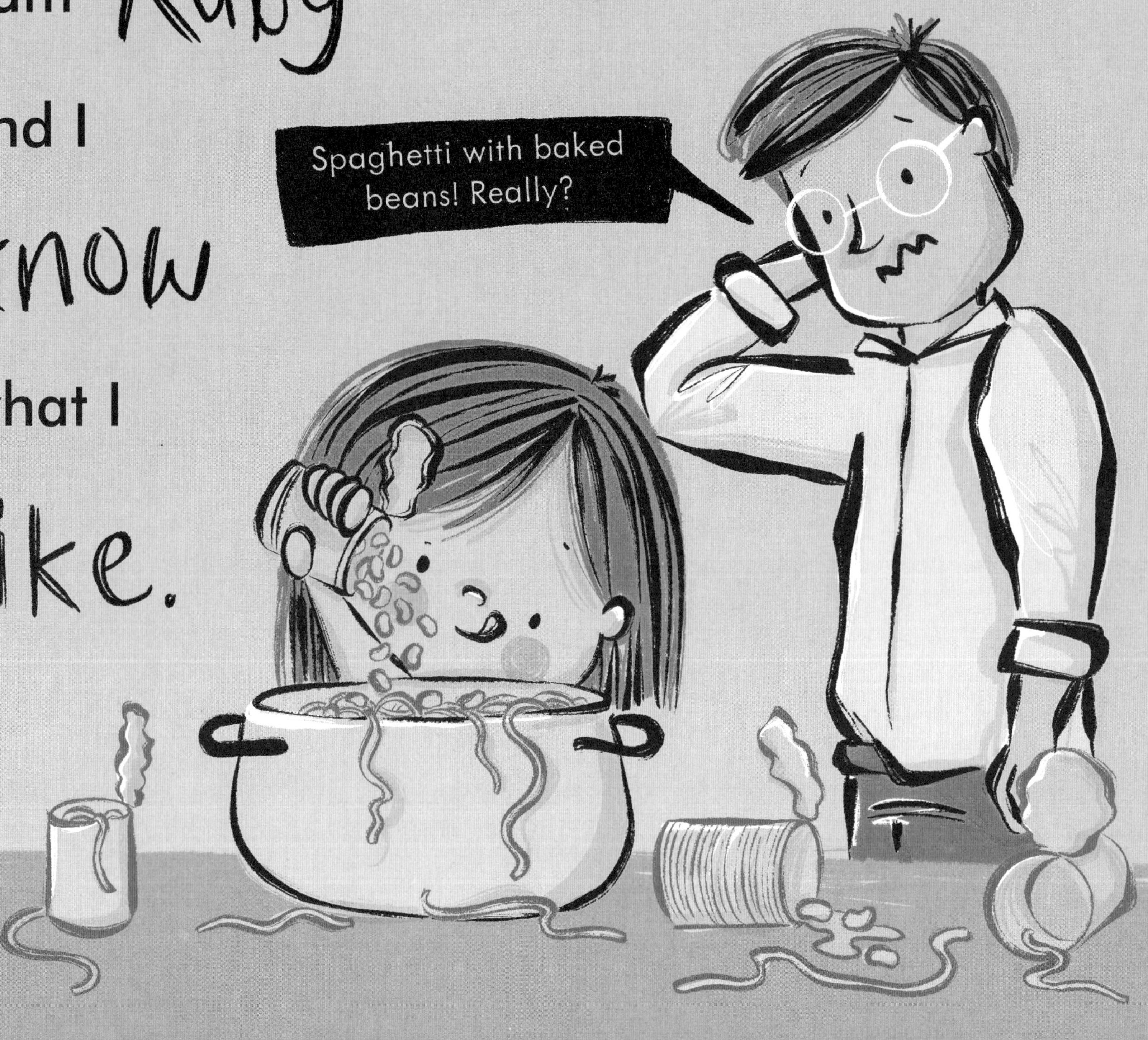

Sometimes Mum and Dad need help.

It's a **good** thing
I'm here!

At the end of the day, I am **full of** beans

and
I
am
not
tired

at aaaall

Which is a good thing

because there is **still** . . .

a lot to do.

MUuuuUUUuM

But they're
forgetting
something . . .

I am Ruby and I know exactly what I want.